Dedicated to our delightful granddaughters, Layla and Kezi.

May God use these cartoons to give you both a deep love for God and a desire to please Him with all of your choices!

Mimi and Grandpa

Published by Mission Minded Publishers for UnveilinGLORY
© 2017 ❖ Sjogren and Sjogren
First Printing, January 2017

      Mission Minded Publishers
      4663 Crown Hill Rd.
      Mechanicsville, VA 23111

ISBN: 978-0-9973110-7-5

To order additional copies, contact UnveilinGLORY at 804.781.0386 or go online at www.UnveilinGLORY.com/bookstore

Welcome to UnveilinGLORY's third cartoon book. If you're new to *Cat and Dog Theology*, you're probably wondering, "What is this all about?" *Cat and Dog Theology* helps you see the differences between a God-centered and a people-centered Christianity. Both are found in the church. Its basis is found in a simple joke about the differences between a cat and a dog.

A dog says, "You pet me, you feed me, you shelter me, you love me. **You** must be God."

A cat says, "You pet me, you feed me, you shelter me, you love me. **I** must be God."

The joke asks a simple question. Do we live for God or does God live for us? Two different answers bring about two totally different Christian attitudes and lifestyles.

Dogs pray to advance God's kingdom. Cats ask God to advance their kingdom.

Dogs seek to make God famous. Cats ask God to make them famous.

Dogs serve God. Cats expect God to serve them.

Dogs ask, "What can I do for God?" Cats ask, "What can God do for me?"

Dogs seek God's face. Cats seek His hand.

Dogs primarily want God. Cats primarily want God's blessings.

These differences can change your entire Christianity. It can change the way you parent your child. It can change the way your child grows up. It can change everything! This book was specifically created to help you with the character development of the children in your life so that they might choose to live for the glory of God. It is the third of three cartoon books we have created.

III

There are three ways you can use these cartoons:

1. Simply discuss the cartoon with your children and talk about the different attitudes.
2. Don't let them see the cartoon, but give them the scenario and tell them the "topic" at the top. Ask them how they think the Cat would respond and how they think the Dog would respond without letting them see the answers. Then discuss the differences between their answer and the answers given. (Who knows, their answer may be better than the cartoon book's answer itself!)
3. Before or after they read it, have them act out both the Dog's attitude and the Cat's attitude. In acting it out, they are much more likely to remember the differences between Cat attitudes and Dog attitudes. Feel free to ham it up with them!

Please note that we all wrestle with Cat attitudes (we call them "Cattitudes") in our lives. This is because we all have an old nature inside of us that has a natural tendency to rebel. Even the Apostle Paul wrestled with his old nature as an adult (see Romans 7:21-23.)

Though we seek perfection (Matthew 5:48), don't demand it from your children. Do expect to begin to see more Dog attitudes than Cat attitudes as they grow older. When the "Cattitudes" do reveal themselves, extend lots of grace to them (along with loving discipline if needed) knowing we all wrestle with "catness" inside of us.

We pray you'll have a fantastic time using this cartoon book to train your kids in Cat and Dog Theology! (Please note that *Cat and Dog Theology* is also in coloring book form, DVD form and other forms as well! See our website at: www.UnveilinGLORY.com/bookstore.)

iv

When the babysitter says it is time for bed...

11

When your best friend breaks his arm...

When you accidentally break your mom's favorite tea cup...

Don't worry. I'll clean it up fast, and she'll never know.

Mom, I'm sorry. I accidentally broke your favorite tea cup.

When told to wait until age 13 before using makeup...

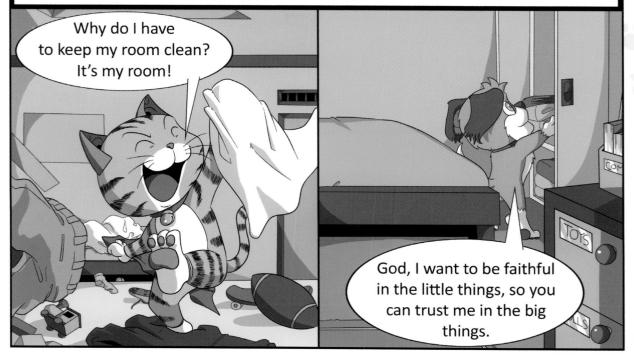

53

When Mom asks you
to put your clean clothes away...

That's good enough. What does it matter if I do an excellent job or not?

God says if I'm faithful in the little things here, he'll be able to trust me with big things in heaven!

When Mom wakes you up in the morning...

When your sibling fails a math test...

When someone is sitting on the buddy bench at school...

What a loser. No one wants to play with him.

Hey, he needs a friend. Let's go ask if he wants to jump rope with us.

When a grandparent comes to visit...

I hate it when Grandma comes to visit. Mom makes us listen to her stories.

Grandma, here are your slippers. Tell us a story about when you were a child.

85

When dreaming about
future rewards in heaven...

When dreaming about worshipping God in heaven...

97

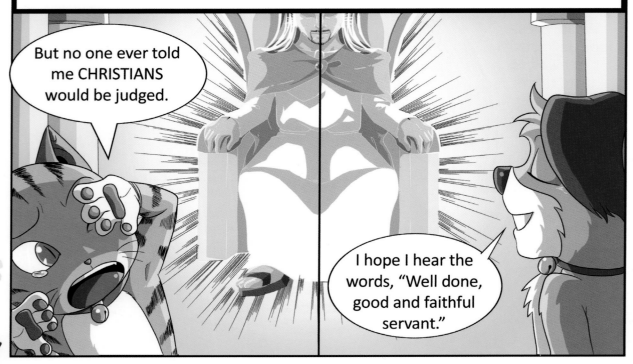

When our lives are judged by Jesus...

When we get to heaven, we will serve God in many different ways...

Thanks for reading
103 Cat and Dog Choices!

Check these out if you haven't already!

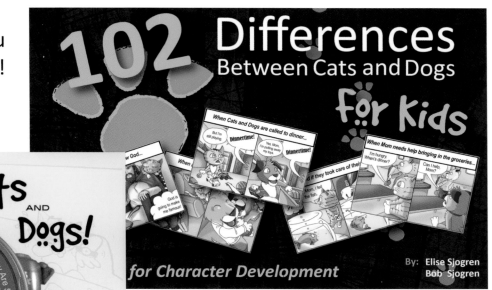

Never Forget...

Check out our
eight homeschool curriculum
at:
www.CatandDogTheology.org
for kids grades K-12.